COPYMASTERS

Stage 2

Blue Level

Written by
Rose Griffiths

Heinemann is an imprint of Pearson Education Limited, a company incorporated in England and Wales, having its registered office at Edinburgh Gate, Harlow, Essex, CM20 2JE. Registered company number: 872828

www.heinemann.co.uk

Heinemann is a registered trademark of Pearson Education Limited

Text © Rose Griffiths 1996, 2005, 2009

First published 1996
Second edition first published 2005
Third edition first published 2009

18
10

British Library Cataloguing in Publication Data
A catalogue record for this book is available from the British Library.

ISBN 978 0 435912 46 8

Designed by Anna Stasinska
Original illustrations © Pearson Education Ltd 2009
Illustrated by Martin Chatterton, Pet Gotohda and Matt Buckley
Printed in the UK by Ashford Colour Press

Acknowledgements
We would like to thank Queens Dyke Primary, Witney, Oxfordshire for their invaluable help in the development and trialling of this course.

Every effort has been made to contact copyright holders of material reproduced in this book. Any omissions will be rectified in subsequent printings if notice is given to the publishers.

Websites
The websites used in this book were correct and up-to-date at the time of publication. It is essential for tutors to preview each website before using it in class so as to ensure that the URL is still accurate, relevant and appropriate. We suggest that tutors bookmark useful websites and consider enabling students to access them through the school/college intranet.

 Contents

Fill the box

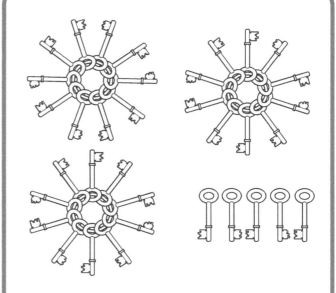

How many paperclips?_____

How many keys? _____

Draw the missing things.

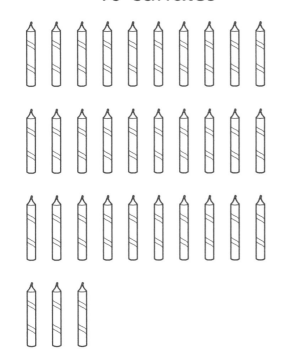

40 candles

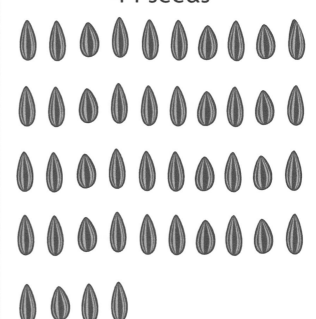

49 seeds

B1

More or less

Join the dots.
Start from 40, and work backwards.
40, then 39, then 38, …

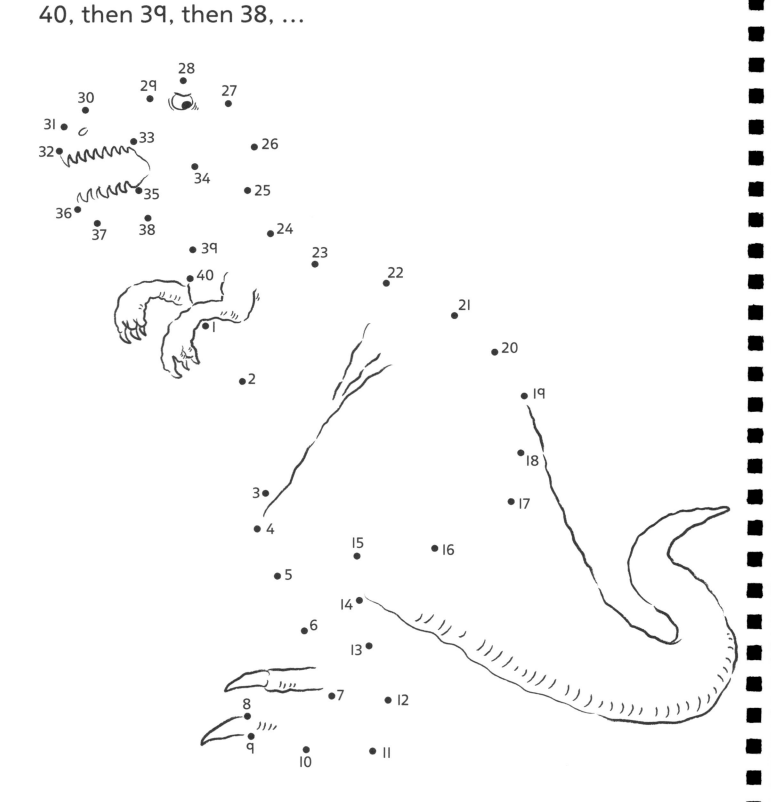

More or less

Fill in the missing numbers.

1	2	3	4			7		9	10
11	12			15	16		18		
	22	23	24				28		30
31		33		35		37		39	
	42		44		46		48		50

What is one less than 10?

9

What is one less than 20? _____

What is one less than 30? _____

What is one less than 40? _____

What is one less than 50? _____

Name: _____   Date: _____

Spelling numbers

Fill in the missing letters.

1

o n e
o n _
o _ _ _
_ _ _ _
o n e

2

t w o
t w _
t _ _ _
_ _ _ _
t w o

3

t h r e e
t h _ _ _
t h _ _ _
_ _ r e e
_ _ r e e
_ _ _ _ _
t h r e e

4

f o u r
f _ _ _ _
f _ _ _ _
f _ _ _ r
_ o u r
_ _ _ _ _
f o u r

5

f i v e
f _ _ _ _
f _ _ _ _
f i _ _ _
_ i v e
_ _ _ _ _
f i v e

Mixed up numbers! Sort them out.

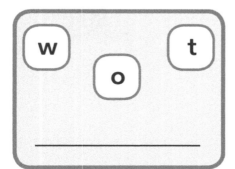

_____

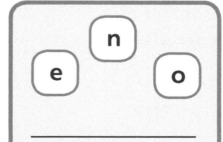

_____

o   u
f
r

_____

Spelling numbers

Fill in the missing letters.

6

s i x
s i _
s ___
___ ___
s i x

10

t e n
t e _
t ___
___ ___
t e n

7

s e v e n
s e ____
s e ____
__ v e n
__ v e n
_____
s e v e n

8

e i g h t
e i ____
e i ____
__ g h t
__ g h t
_____
e i g h t

q

n i n e
n i ___
n i ___
n ____
n ____
_____
n i n e

Mixed up numbers! Sort them out.

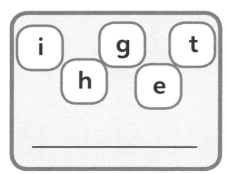

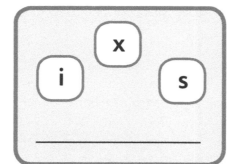

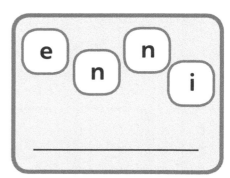

Name: _____ Date: _____

Eight bats

Cut out the numbers at the bottom.

Stick them in the right spaces.

2 + ☐ = 8

3 + ☐ = 8

0 + ☐ = 8

6 + ☐ = 8

1 + ☐ = 8

5 + ☐ = 8

7 + ☐ = 8

4 + ☐ = 8

✂ -

| 1 | 2 | 3 | 4 | 5 | 6 | 7 | 8 |

Text © Rose Griffiths 2009
Pearson Education Ltd

Addition bonds to 8

◄ Blue Pupil Book Part 1 pages 14 and 15
Copymaster B7

Name: _____   Date: _____

Eight bats

Eight bats!

Don't be silly!

Fill in the missing numbers.

3 + ☐ = 8

1 + ☐ = 8

5 + ☐ = 8

2 + ☐ = 8

7 + ☐ = 8

4 + ☐ = 8

6 + ☐ = 8

☐ + 3 = 8

☐ + 7 = 8

☐ + 0 = 8

☐ + 4 = 8

☐ + 6 = 8

☐ + 2 = 8

☐ + 5 = 8

2 + ☐ = 8

☐ + 2 = 8

6 + ☐ = 8

☐ + 6 = 8

3 + ☐ = 8

☐ + 3 = 8

5 + ☐ = 8

☐ + 5 = 8

Text © Rose Griffiths 2009
Pearson Education Ltd

B7

Name: _____   Date: _____

Number links

Use bricks to do these.

1   6   7

1 + 6 = _____

6 + 1 = _____

7 – 1 = _____

7 – 6 = _____

2   6   8

2 + 6 = _____

6 + 2 = _____

8 – 2 = _____

8 – 6 = _____

3   5   8

3 + 5 = _____

5 + 3 = _____

8 – 3 = _____

8 – 5 = _____

1   4   5

1 + 4 = _____

4 + 1 = _____

5 – 1 = _____

5 – 4 = _____

Make up 4 sums with these:

2   4   6

2   4   6

_____ + _____ = _____

_____ + _____ = _____

_____ – _____ = _____

_____ – _____ = _____

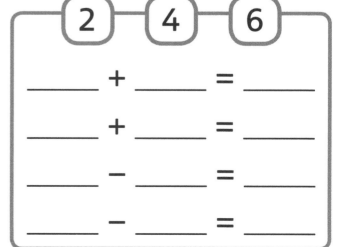

Links between addition and subtraction

◀ Blue Pupil Book Part 1 pages 16 and 17
Copymaster B9

Number links

5 + 3 = _____

3 + 5 = _____

8 – 5 = _____

8 – 3 = _____

1 + 5 = _____

5 + 1 = _____

6 – 5 = _____

6 – 1 = _____

3 + 4 = _____

4 + 3 = _____

7 – 3 = _____

7 – 4 = _____

5 + 2 = _____

2 + 5 = _____

7 – 2 = _____

7 – 5 = _____

2 + 6 = _____

6 + 2 = _____

8 – 2 = _____

8 – 6 = _____

2 + 4 = _____

4 + 2 = _____

6 – 2 = _____

6 – 4 = _____

3 + 3 = _____

6 – 3 = _____

1 + 7 = _____

7 + 1 = _____

8 – 1 = _____

8 – 7 = _____

4 + 4 = _____

8 – 4 = _____

Links between addition and subtraction

Text © Rose Griffiths 2009
Pearson Education Ltd

B9

Name: _____   Date: _____

Off by heart

1 + 0 = _____

1 + 1 = _____

1 + 2 = _____

1 + 3 = _____

1 + 4 = _____

1 + 5 = _____

1 + 6 = _____

1 + 7 = _____

2 + 0 = _____

2 + 1 = _____

2 + 2 = _____

2 + 3 = _____

2 + 4 = _____

2 + 5 = _____

2 + 6 = _____

3 + 0 = _____

3 + 1 = _____

3 + 2 = _____

3 + 3 = _____

3 + 4 = _____

3 + 5 = _____

4 + 0 = _____

4 + 1 = _____

4 + 2 = _____

4 + 3 = _____

4 + 4 = _____

6 + 0 = _____

6 + 1 = _____

6 + 2 = _____

5 + 0 = _____

5 + 1 = _____

5 + 2 = _____

5 + 3 = _____

How many of the sums do you know off by heart?

_____

B10   Text © Rose Griffiths 2009
Pearson Education Ltd   Mental recall of addition within 8   ◄ Blue Pupil Book Part 1 pages 18 and 19

Spiders and snakes

Each spider is made with ten pipecleaners.
How many pipecleaners in each box?

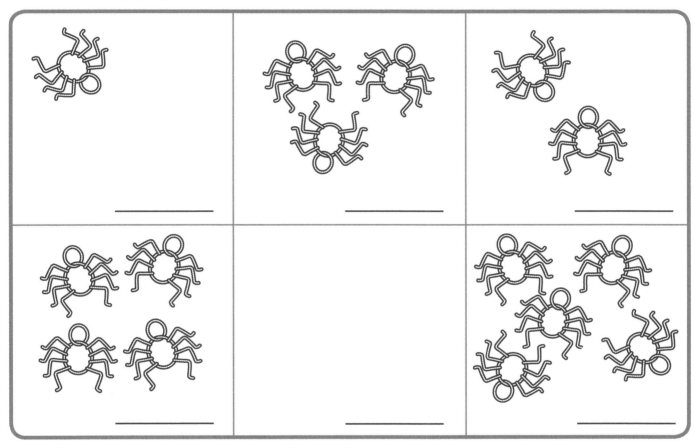

How many pipecleaners?

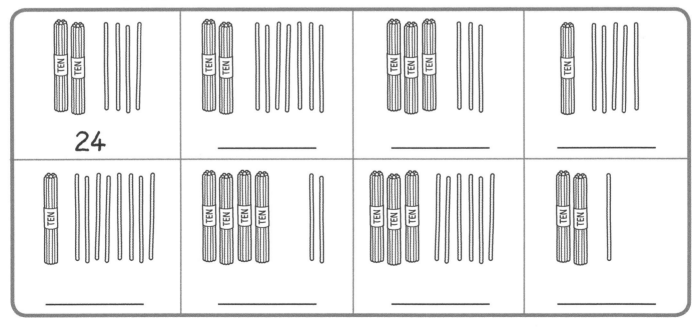

24

Name: _____ Date: _____

Spiders and snakes

Each snake is made with two pipecleaners.
How many pipecleaners in each box?

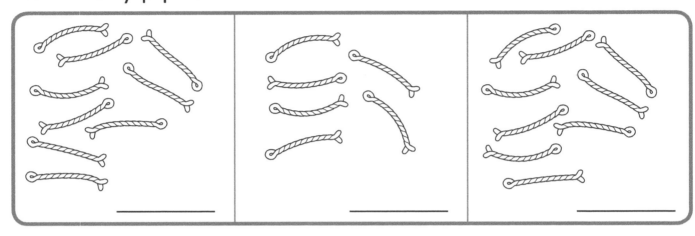

_____   _____   _____

Fill in the chart.

	How many snakes?	How many pipecleaners?

What comes next?

2, 4, 6, 8, _____

20, 22, 24, _____

32, 34, 36, 38, _____

42, 44, 46, _____, _____,

Text © Rose Griffiths 2009
Pearson Education Ltd
Multiples of 2 and 10 to 50 ◄Blue Pupil Book Part 1 pages 20 and 21

Speedy sums A   3 minute test

Name: _____   Date: _____

4 + 2 = _____	5 + 2 = _____	2 + 2 = _____
3 + 4 = _____	1 + 6 = _____	0 + 7 = _____
1 + 3 = _____	2 + 5 = _____	4 + 3 = _____
6 + 1 = _____	0 + 2 = _____	3 + 2 = _____
2 + 3 = _____	4 + 1 = _____	3 + 3 = _____
5 + 0 = _____	2 + 4 = _____	1 + 4 = _____
3 + 1 = _____	1 + 5 = _____	Score: _____

Speedy sums B   3 minute test

Name: _____   Date: _____

2 + 5 = _____	4 – 2 = _____	1 + 2 = _____
4 + 2 = _____	7 – 3 = _____	5 – 4 = _____
0 + 6 = _____	5 – 5 = _____	3 + 3 = _____
2 + 3 = _____	6 – 0 = _____	6 – 2 = _____
6 + 1 = _____	7 – 4 = _____	7 + 0 = _____
4 + 3 = _____	3 – 1 = _____	6 – 3 = _____
1 + 3 = _____	7 – 2 = _____	Score: _____

Name: _____ Date: _____

Speedy sums C   1 2 3 minute test

2 + 6 = _____   7 – 3 = _____   4 + 4 = _____

4 + 2 = _____   6 – 6 = _____   5 – 2 = _____

1 + 1 = _____   8 – 7 = _____   3 + 3 = _____

3 + 5 = _____   4 – 1 = _____   8 – 6 = _____

2 + 3 = _____   8 – 2 = _____   4 + 0 = _____

3 + 4 = _____   7 – 5 = _____   8 – 3 = _____

2 + 5 = _____   7 – 0 = _____   Score: _____

Name: _____ Date: _____

Speedy sums D   1 2 3 minute test

2 + 4 = _____   7 – 2 = _____   3 + 0 = _____

3 + 3 = _____   6 – 5 = _____   5 – 3 = _____

6 + 2 = _____   8 – 8 = _____   4 + 4 = _____

5 + 3 = _____   5 – 1 = _____   8 – 5 = _____

1 + 1 = _____   4 – 2 = _____   1 + 3 = _____

4 + 3 = _____   7 – 4 = _____   8 – 4 = _____

3 + 2 = _____   7 – 1 = _____   Score: _____

T-shirts

Make up prices for these t-shirts.
Ask a partner to do the questions.

These questions are for _____

£

How much change? _____

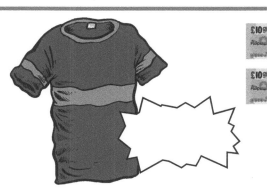

How much change? _____

How much change? _____

How much change? _____

How much change? _____

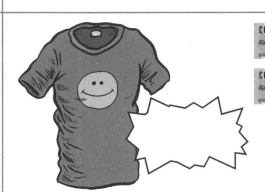

How much change? _____

T-shirts

Name: _____ Date: _____

Make up prices for these t-shirts.
Ask a partner to do the questions.

✂- -

These questions are for _____

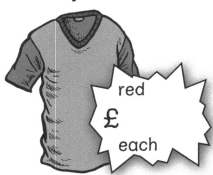

red
£
each

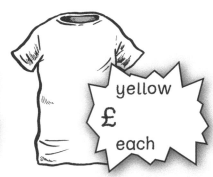

yellow
£
each

blue
£
each

I bought a red t-shirt and a yellow one.

How much did I spend? _____

I bought two red t-shirts and a blue t-shirt.

How much did I spend? _____

I bought 2 yellow t-shirts.

How much did I spend? _____

I bought a blue t-shirt and a yellow one.

How much did I spend? _____

Text © Rose Griffiths 2009
Pearson Education Ltd

Addition and subtraction within 20

◀ Blue Pupil Book Part I pages 24 and 25

Bowling

Fill in the missing numbers.

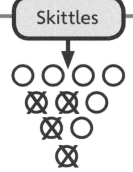

Skittles

Knocked down: **4**
Still standing: **6**
——
10

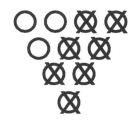

Knocked down:
Still standing: ____
____

Knocked down:
Still standing: ____
____

Knocked down:
Still standing: ____
____

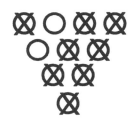

Knocked down:
Still standing: ____
____

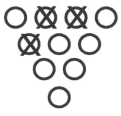

Knocked down:
Still standing: ____
____

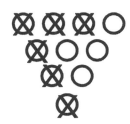

Knocked down:
Still standing: ____
____

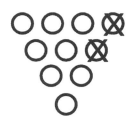

Knocked down:
Still standing: ____
____

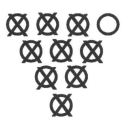

Knocked down:
Still standing: ____
____

Fives and ones

Draw the missing 5p coins.

25p	**35p** 

40p

50p	**45p**

B18

Text © Rose Griffiths 2009
Pearson Education Ltd

Counting in 5s to 50

◀ Blue Pupil Book Part I pages 28 and 29
Copymaster B19

Fives and ones

Fill in the missing numbers.
Use coins to help you.

5p + 5p = _____   10p + 5p = _____

15p + 5p = _____   20p + 5p = _____

25p + 5p = _____   30p + 5p = _____

35p + 5p = _____   40p + 5p = _____

45p + 5p = _____

10p + 10p = _____   15p + 15p = _____

20p + 20p = _____   25p + 25p = _____

5, 10, _____ , 20, 25, _____ , 35, _____ , 45, _____ .

5, _____ , 15, 20, _____ , 30, _____ , 40, _____ , _____ .

Name: _____   Date: _____

Pick up bricks

Draw the missing bricks.

15 bricks

▢▢▢▢▢▢▢▢▢▢▢▢▢

▢ ▢

23 bricks

▢▢▢▢▢▢▢▢▢▢▢

▢▢▢▢▢▢▢▢▢▢

31 bricks

▢▢▢▢▢▢▢▢▢▢▢▢

▢▢▢▢▢▢▢▢▢▢▢

39 bricks

▢▢▢▢▢▢▢▢▢▢▢▢

▢▢▢▢▢▢▢▢▢▢▢

▢▢▢▢▢▢▢▢▢▢▢

▢ ▢

42 bricks

▢▢▢▢▢▢▢▢▢▢

▢▢▢▢▢▢▢▢▢▢

▢▢▢▢▢▢▢▢▢▢

50 bricks

▢▢▢▢▢▢▢▢▢▢▢

▢▢▢▢▢▢▢▢▢▢

I had three turns.

| 1st turn | 2nd turn | 3rd turn |
I got 37 bricks.   I got 44 bricks.   I got 41 bricks.

Which turn did I get the most bricks? _____

Pick up bricks

Count the bricks.

Do the sums.

$10 + 1 =$ _____

$10 + 2 =$ _____

$10 + 3 =$ _____

$10 + 4 =$ _____

$10 + 5 =$ _____

$10 + 6 =$ _____

$10 + 7 =$ _____

$10 + 8 =$ _____

$10 + 9 =$ _____

$10 + 10 =$ _____

$20 - 2 =$ _____

$20 - 4 =$ _____

$20 - 6 =$ _____

$20 - 8 =$ _____

$20 - 10 =$ _____

 Check

Bats and fives

Fill in the missing numbers.

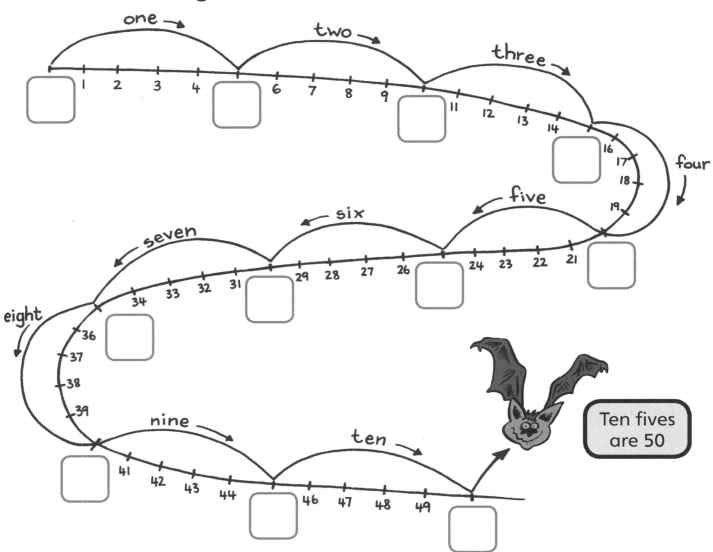

Ten fives are 50

Check

$5 + 5 =$	— Two fives —	$2 \times 5 =$
$5 + 5 + 5 =$	— Three fives —	$3 \times 5 =$
$5 + 5 + 5 + 5 =$	— Four fives —	$4 \times 5 =$
$5 + 5 + 5 + 5 + 5 =$	— Five fives —	$5 \times 5 =$

Bats and fives

Fill in the missing numbers.

1	2	3	4	5	6	7	8	9	
11	12	13	14		16	17	18	19	
21	22	23	24		26	27	28	29	
31	32	33	34		36	37	38	39	
41	42	43	44		46	47	48	49	

10 times 5

Ten fives	$10 \times 5 =$		Five fives	$5 \times 5 =$
Nine fives	$9 \times 5 =$		Four fives	$4 \times 5 =$
Eight fives	$8 \times 5 =$		Three fives	$3 \times 5 =$
Seven fives	$7 \times 5 =$		Two fives	$2 \times 5 =$
Six fives	$6 \times 5 =$		One five	$1 \times 5 =$
			No fives	$0 \times 5 =$

Text © Rose Griffiths 2009
Pearson Education Ltd

B23

Card sums

Cut out these cards. Use them with Copymaster B25.

A ◇	2 ◇◇	3 ◇◇◇	4 ◇◇◇◇	5 ◇◇◇◇◇
6 ◇◇◇◇◇◇	7 ◇◇◇◇◇◇◇	8 ◇◇◇◇◇◇◇◇	9 ◇◇◇◇◇◇◇◇◇	10 ◇◇◇◇◇◇◇◇◇◇
A ♣	2 ♣♣	3 ♣♣♣	4 ♣♣♣♣	5 ♣♣♣♣♣
6 ♣♣♣♣♣♣	7 ♣♣♣♣♣♣♣	8 ♣♣♣♣♣♣♣♣	9 ♣♣♣♣♣♣♣♣♣	10 ♣♣♣♣♣♣♣♣♣♣

Addition within 20
◄ Blue Pupil Book Part I pages 34 and 35
Copymaster B25

Card sums

You need the cards made from Copymaster 24.
Find cards to make each sum. Stick them on.

| 2 cards which add up to 20. | 2 cards which add up to 17. |

| 2 cards which add up to 10. | 2 cards which add up to 14. |

Work with a partner.
Make up some sums like these for each other.
Use the rest of your cards.

Sums which make 8

Print these on card. You can use them again.
Cut out the instructions cards, 34 number cards and 3 sum cards.
You can keep them in an envelope or a clear zip-top wallet.

Sums which make 8

A game for 1, 2 or 3 people.

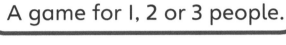

- **Before you start**
  Take a sum card each.
  Shuffle the number cards.
  Put them in a pile on the table, face down.

- **How to play**
  Can you make 4 different sums which make 8?

Take the top number card. Put it on your sum card, <u>or</u> (if you don't want it) put it at the bottom of the pile.

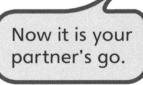

Now it is your partner's go.

- **Keep going until you have all filled your cards.**
  Who finished first?

Blue Pupil Book Part 1; **Mental recall of addition within 8**

Text © Rose Griffiths 2009
Pearson Education Ltd

Sums which make 8

Print these on card. You can use them again.

0	1	1	2	2
0	1	1	2	2
3	3	4	4	4
3	3	4	4	4
5	5	6	6	7
5	5	6	6	7
8	8		7	7

Text © Rose Griffiths 2009
Pearson Education Ltd

Sums which make 8

Print 3 copies of these on card. You can use them again.

Sums which make 8

☐ + ☐ = **8**

☐ + ☐ = **8**

☐ + ☐ = **8**

☐ + ☐ = **8**

◀ Blue Pupil Book Part I: use from pages 18 and 19 onwards

Fifty pence game

Print these on card. You can use them again.
Cut out the instructions card and 16 playing cards.
You can keep them in an envelope or a clear zip-top wallet.

Fifty pence

A game for I, 2 or 3 people.

- **Before you start**
  Shuffle the cards.
  Spread them out on the table, face down.

- **How to play**

Turn over 3 cards.
Count the money.

If you get exactly 50p,
keep the cards.
If not, turn the cards
back over.

Now it is your
partner's go.

- **Keep going until no one can make any more fifty pences.**

Blue Pupil Book Part I; **Counting in 5s to 50**

Fifty pence

Fifty pence

Fifty pence

Fifty pence

Fifty pence game

Print these on card. You can use them again.

Fifty pence

Fifty pence

Fifty pence

Fifty pence

Fifty pence

Fifty pence

Fifty pence

Fifty pence

Fifty pence

Fifty pence

Fifty pence

Fifty pence

◀ Blue Pupil Book Part I; use from pages 28 and 29 onwards

Ⓣ Ⓖ

Coins in a jar

How much money?

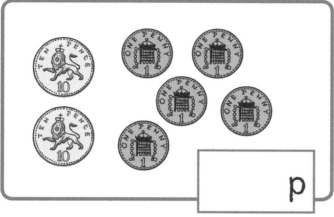

p

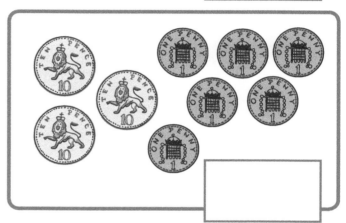

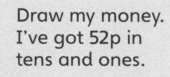

Draw my money.
I've got 23p in
tens and ones.

Draw my money.
I've got 52p in
tens and ones.

Name: _____   Date: _____

Sums in words

Fill in the missing letters.

11

eleven
elev___
el_____
e _____
eleven

12

twelve
twel___
tw_____
t_____
twelve

13

thirteen
thir_____
th _____
_____teen
th _____
_____
thirteen

14

fourteen
four_____
f_____
_____teen
f_____
_____
fourteen

15

fifteen
fif_____
f _____
f___teen
f _____
_____
fifteen

Mixed up numbers! Sort them out.

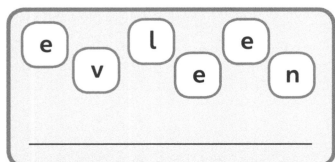

_____   _____

Text © Rose Griffiths 2009
Pearson Education Ltd

Spelling eleven to twenty

◀ Blue Pupil Book Part 2 pages 40 and 41
Copymaster B33

Sums in words

Fill in the missing letters.

16

s i x t e e n

s i x _____

s _____

_____

s i x t e e n

17

s e v e n t e e n

s e v e n _____

s e v_____

s _____

s e v e n t e e n

18

e i g h t e e n

e i g h t_____

e i _____

_____t e e n

e_____

_____

e i g h t e e n

19

n i n e t e e n

n i n e _____

n_____

_____t e e n

n_____

_____

n i n e t e e n

20

t w e n t y

t w e n_____

t w_____

_____t y

t _____

_____

t w e n t y

Mixed up numbers! Sort them out.

w e t
n   t y

t x n i
e e s

Tens and ones

Make each number with tens and ones.

Draw it.

	Then add one.
18	
	18 + 1 = ____
49	
	49 + 1 = ____
23	
	23 + 1 = ____
31	
	31 + 1 = ____
42	
	42 + 1 = ____
30	
	30 + 1 = ____

Tens and ones

Make each number with tens and ones.

Draw it.

| 18 |
| 49 |
| 23 |
| 31 |
| 42 |
| 30 |

Then add ten.

18 + 10 = _____

49 + 10 = _____

23 + 10 = _____

31 + 10 = _____

42 + 10 = _____

30 + 10 = _____

Name: _____   Date: _____

Two times table

Cut out the eleven tables facts.
Fold along the dotted line and glue flat.

Ask your teacher how to practise with these.

		5 × 2	10
0 × 2	0	6 × 2	12
1 × 2	2	7 × 2	14
2 × 2	4	8 × 2	16
3 × 2	6	9 × 2	18
4 × 2	8	10 × 2	20

Two times table

Fill in the missing numbers.
Check with a calculator.

$5 \times 2 =$ ☐
$2 \times 5 =$ ☐

$8 \times 2 =$ ☐
$2 \times 8 =$ ☐

$3 \times 2 =$ ☐
$2 \times 3 =$ ☐

$10 \times 2 =$ ☐
$2 \times 10 =$ ☐

$10 \times 2 =$ ☐
☐ $\times 2 = 18$
$8 \times 2 =$ ☐
$7 \times$ ☐ $= 14$
☐ $\times 2 = 12$
$5 \times 2 =$ ☐
$4 \times 2 =$ ☐
☐ $\times 2 = 6$
$2 \times$ ☐ $= 4$
$1 \times 2 =$ ☐
$0 \times 2 =$ ☐

What is
7 times 2?

What is
2 times 7?

_____   _____

Text © Rose Griffiths 2009
Pearson Education Ltd

B37

Name: _____   Date: _____

Hours and half hours

Use a real clock.

Make your clock show each time. Then draw it.

One o'clock	Half past one	Two o'clock
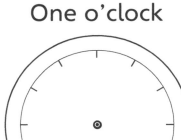	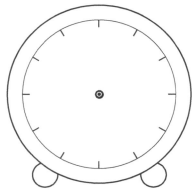	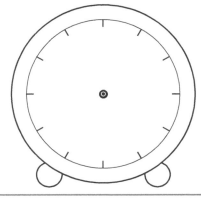
Half past two	Three o'clock	Half past three
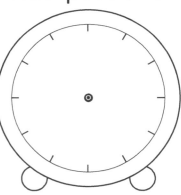	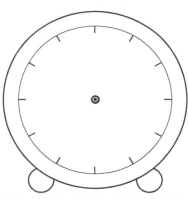	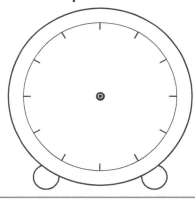
Four o'clock	Half past four	Five o'clock
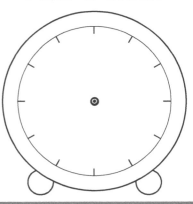	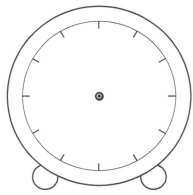	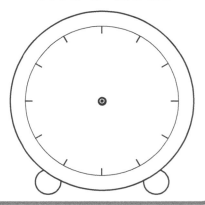

Text © Rose Griffiths 2009
Pearson Education Ltd   **Using halves; telling the time** ◄ Blue Pupil Book Part 2 pages 46 and 47
Copymaster B39

Hours and half hours

What's the time?

4 o'clock   Half past ____

Nine counters

Colour the counters red or blue. Make each box different.

Then fill in the missing numbers.

__3__ red, __6__ blue

$$3 + 6 = \quad 9$$

___ red, ___ blue

$$\boxed{} + \boxed{} = \underline{}$$

___ red, ___ blue

$$\boxed{} + \boxed{} = \underline{}$$

___ red, ___ blue

$$\boxed{} + \boxed{} = \underline{}$$

___ red, ___ blue

$$\boxed{} + \boxed{} = \underline{}$$

___ red, ___ blue

$$\boxed{} + \boxed{} = \underline{}$$

Addition bonds to 9

◀ Blue Pupil Book Part 2 pages 48 and 49
Copymaster B41

Nine counters

Fill in the missing numbers.

$2 + \boxed{} = 9$

$4 + \boxed{} = 9$

$6 + \boxed{} = 9$

$3 + \boxed{} = 9$

$8 + \boxed{} = 9$

$5 + \boxed{} = 9$

$1 + \boxed{} = 9$

$7 + \boxed{} = 9$

$\boxed{} + 0 = 9$

$\boxed{} + 5 = 9$

$\boxed{} + 3 = 9$

$\boxed{} + 6 = 9$

$\boxed{} + 2 = 9$

$\boxed{} + 4 = 9$

$\boxed{} + 8 = 9$

$\boxed{} + 7 = 9$

$4 + \boxed{} = 9$

$\boxed{} + 4 = 9$

$5 + \boxed{} = 9$

$\boxed{} + 5 = 9$

$6 + \boxed{} = 9$

$\boxed{} + 6 = 9$

$3 + \boxed{} = 9$

$\boxed{} + 3 = 9$

B41

Name: _____ Date: _____

Fives and tens

Fill in the four missing numbers.

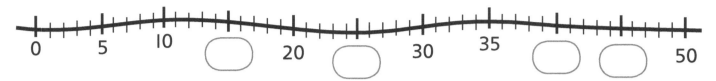

Use the number line like this:

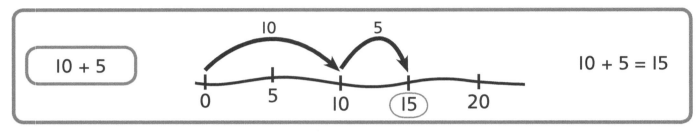

10 + 5   10 + 5 = 15

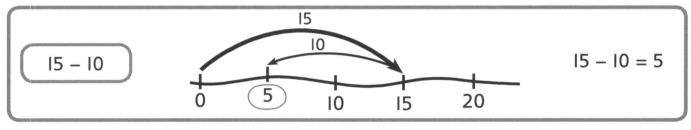

15 − 10   15 − 10 = 5

10 + 10 = _____	20 − 15 = _____
10 + 15 = _____	30 − 10 = _____
20 + 15 = _____	45 − 5 = _____
15 + 20 = _____	50 − 10 = _____
15 + 25 = _____	45 − 20 = _____
25 + 25 = _____	45 − 15 = _____
25 + 10 = _____	30 − 15 = _____
45 + 5 = _____	25 − 20 = _____

Text © Rose Griffiths 2009
Pearson Education Ltd
Using 5s and 10s to 50   ◀ Blue Pupil Book Part 2 pages 50 and 51
Copymaster B43

Name: _____   Date: _____

Fives and tens

Use the number line, then check with a calculator.

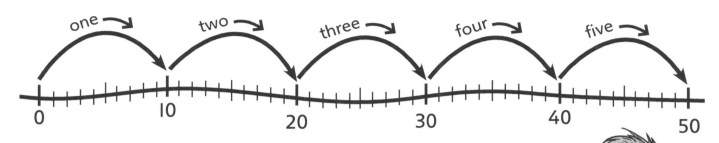

one → two → three → four → five →

0   10   20   30   40   50

| No tens | $0 \times 10 =$ |

Ten times five ...

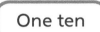

| One ten | $1 \times 10 =$ |

| Two tens | $2 \times 10 =$ |

| Three tens | $3 \times 10 =$ |

| Four tens | $4 \times 10 =$ |

| Five tens | $5 \times 10 =$ |

$10 \times 5 =$ _____

$10 \times 4 =$ _____

$10 \times 3 =$ _____

$10 \times 2 =$ _____

$10 \times 1 =$ _____

$10 \times 0 =$ _____

$2 \times 10 =$ _____

$4 \times 10 =$ _____

$3 \times 10 =$ _____

$0 \times 10 =$ _____

$5 \times 10 =$ _____

Check

$10 \times 1 =$ _____

$10 \times 3 =$ _____

$10 \times 5 =$ _____

$10 \times 4 =$ _____

$10 \times 2 =$ _____

Name: _____ Date: _____

Speedy sums E 1 2 3 minute test

5 + 2 = _____   8 – 3 = _____   3 + 3 = _____

2 + 3 = _____   7 – 6 = _____   5 – 3 = _____

4 + 4 = _____   3 – 3 = _____   4 + 5 = _____

5 + 0 = _____   9 – 5 = _____   8 – 2 = _____

1 + 8 = _____   7 – 2 = _____   3 + 4 = _____

6 + 3 = _____   2 – 1 = _____   6 – 4 = _____

2 + 2 = _____   9 – 2 = _____   Score: _____

Name: _____ Date: _____

Speedy sums F 1 2 3 minute test

6 + 3 = _____   9 – 8 = _____   4 + 4 = _____

4 + 3 = _____   8 – 5 = _____   9 – 4 = _____

3 + 0 = _____   7 – 3 = _____   6 + 2 = _____

2 + 2 = _____   9 – 7 = _____   8 – 3 = _____

5 + 4 = _____   6 – 2 = _____   1 + 5 = _____

2 + 5 = _____   9 – 3 = _____   6 – 5 = _____

4 + 1 = _____   4 – 4 = _____   Score: _____

Boxes

Sunesh and Emma keep playing 'Boxes'.

There are 20 boxes altogether.
How many did I get in each game?

5th game

Sunesh got 15, and Emma got _____ .

6th game

Sunesh got 10, and Emma got _____ .

7th game

Sunesh got 5, and Emma got _____ .

8th game

Sunesh got 0, and Emma got _____ .

Fill in the missing numbers.

$18 + \boxed{} = 20$ $17 + \boxed{} = 20$

$13 + \boxed{} = 20$ $14 + \boxed{} = 20$

$16 + \boxed{} = 20$ $9 + \boxed{} = 20$ Check

$7 + \boxed{} = 20$ $12 + \boxed{} = 20$

Name: ____________________ Date: ____________

Boxes

Play 'Boxes' with a partner. Add up your scores.

1st game

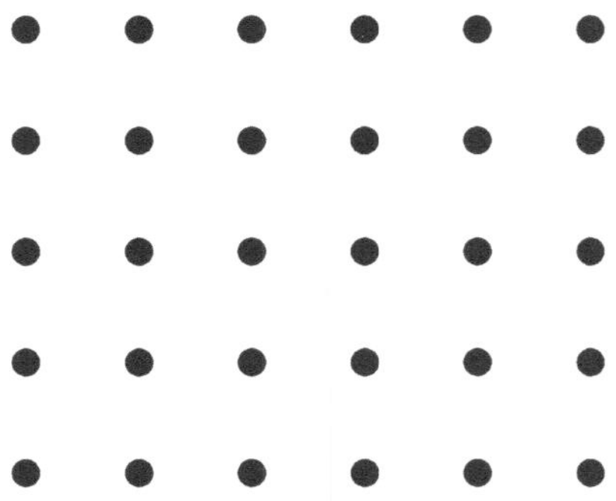

Name	Score
Total	

2nd game

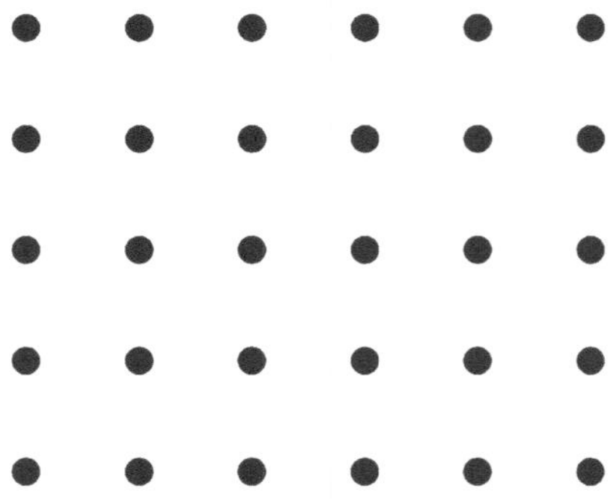

Name	Score
Total	

3rd game

Name	Score
Total	

4th game

Name	Score
Total	

◀ Blue Pupil Book Part 2 pages 54 and 55

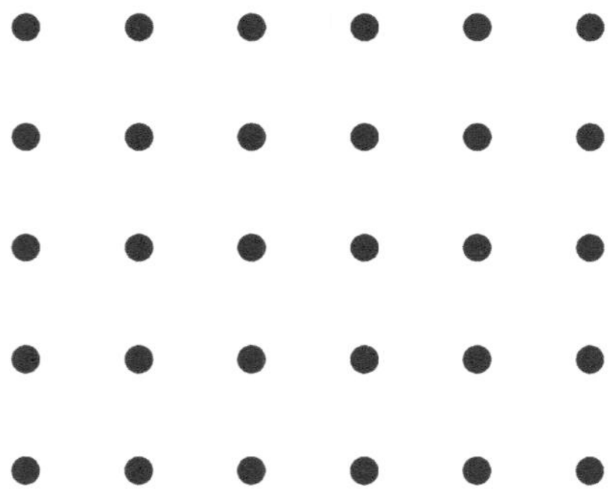

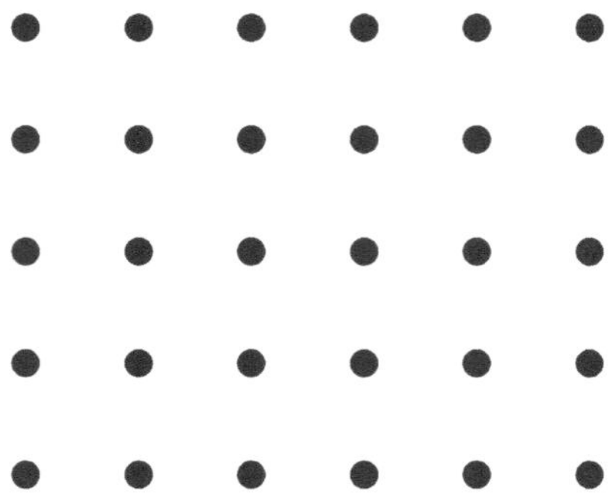

Teen numbers

Write the number and the word.

15 fifteen	

Use tens and ones. Draw them.

16 + 3 =	7 + 11 =
14 + 2 =	10 + 3 =

Name: _____   Date: _____

Teen numbers

Use tens and ones to do each sum.

14 + 5

14 + 5 =

12 + 3

12 + 3 =

6 + 11

6 + 11 =

10 + 7

10 + 7 =

Draw tens and ones.

13 + 4

13 + 4 =

5 + 12

5 + 12 =

8 + 10

8 + 10 =

15 + 3

15 + 3 =

Addition within 20
◄ Blue Pupil Book Part 2 pages 56 and 57

Five times tables

Cut out the eleven tables facts.
Fold along the dotted line and glue flat.

Ask your teacher how to practise with these.

| 5 × 5 | 25 |

0 × 5	0	6 × 5	30
1 × 5	5	7 × 5	35
2 × 5	10	8 × 5	40
3 × 5	15	9 × 5	45
4 × 5	20	10 × 5	50

Five times tables

Fill in the missing numbers.
Check with a calculator.

$3 \times 5 = \boxed{}$

$5 \times 3 = \boxed{}$

$10 \times 5 = \boxed{}$

$5 \times 10 = \boxed{}$

$2 \times 5 = \boxed{}$

$5 \times 2 = \boxed{}$

$7 \times 5 = \boxed{}$

$5 \times 7 = \boxed{}$

$10 \times 5 = \boxed{}$

$\boxed{} \times 5 = 45$

$8 \times 5 = \boxed{}$

$7 \times \boxed{} = 35$

$\boxed{} \times 5 = 30$

$\boxed{} \times 5 = 25$

$4 \times 5 = \boxed{}$

$\boxed{} \times 5 = 15$

$2 \times \boxed{} = 10$

$1 \times 5 = \boxed{}$

$0 \times 5 = \boxed{}$

What is
6 times 5?

_____

What is
5 times 6?

_____

More teen numbers

Use tens and ones.

16 – 3

16 – 3 =

18 – 10

18 – 10 =

15 – 4

15 – 4 =

13 – 3

13 – 3 =

Cross out tens and ones.

14 – 10

14 – 10 =

17 – 11

17 – 11 =

19 – 8

19 – 8 =

16 – 6

16 – 6 =

Text © Rose Griffiths 2009
Pearson Education Ltd

B51

Photos

Name: _____ Date: _____

I took 24 photos.

How many photos of the rabbit? _____

How many photos of my friends? _____

Total: _____

I took 24 photos.

How many photos of the dog? _____

How many photos of my friends? _____

Total: _____

Check

Addition and subtraction within 24 ◄ Blue Pupil Book Part 2 pages 62 and 63
Copymaster B53

Photos

I took 12 photos.

Write or draw to show what was on each photo. Use these clues:

- The first three photos are my cat.
- The 4th, 5th and 6th photos are my friends.
- The 11th and 12th photos are my rabbit.
- There are seven photos of my cat.

1	2	3	4
5	6	7	8
9	10	11	12

What is on the 3rd photo? _____

What is on the 8th photo? _____

What is on the last photo? _____

Name: _____ Date: _____

Fill in this chart.
Remember: one frog scores 3 points.

Frogs in a dish	Draw the missing frogs	Score
0		0
1		3
2		
3		
4		
5		
6		

Text © Rose Griffiths 2009
Pearson Education Ltd

Multiples of 3 to 18

◀ Blue Pupil Book Part 2 pages 64 and 65
Copymaster B55

Hopping frogs

How many counters?

18 _____   _____   _____   _____   _____

0 + 3 = _____	18 – 3 = _____
3 + 3 = _____	15 – 3 = _____
6 + 3 = _____	12 – 3 = _____
9 + 3 = _____	9 – 3 = _____
12 + 3 = _____	6 – 3 = _____
15 + 3 = _____	3 – 3 = _____

3 + 12 = _____	15 + 3 = _____
15 – 3 = _____	18 – 3 = _____
12 + 3 = _____	3 + 15 = _____

Sixty pence

Print this on card. You can use it again.
Colour in the board and cover it with clear plastic if you want.
Cut out the two pieces of the board and stick together.

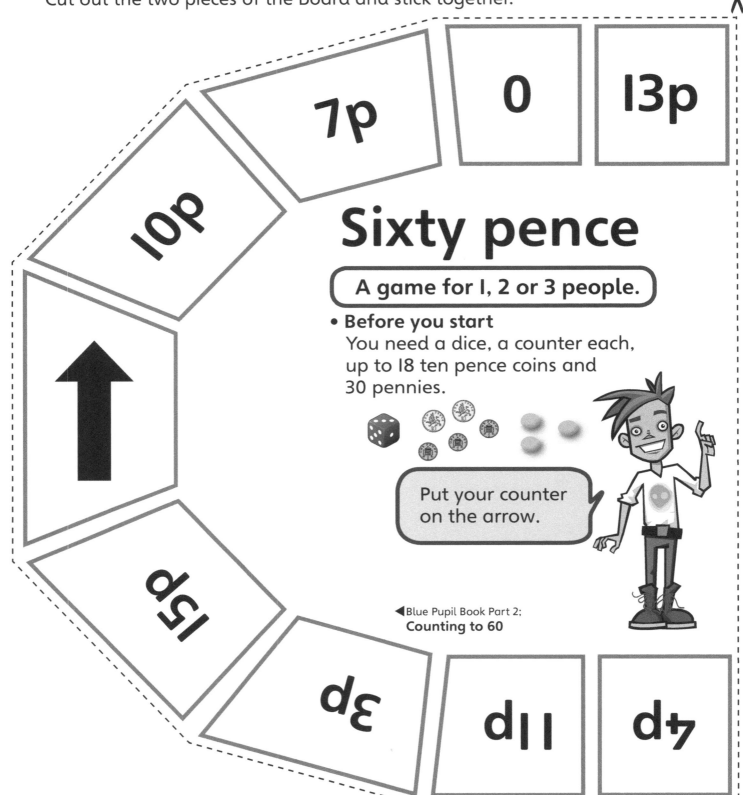

Sixty pence

A game for I, 2 or 3 people.

- **Before you start**
  You need a dice, a counter each, up to 18 ten pence coins and 30 pennies.

  Put your counter on the arrow.

◀ Blue Pupil Book Part 2;
Counting to 60

Text © Rose Griffiths 2009
Pearson Education Ltd
◀ Blue Pupil Book Part 2; use from pages 38 and 39 onwards   (T) (G)

Sixty pence

sheet 2 of 2

Print this on card. You can use it again.
You need a dice, 3 counters, 18 plastic or card ten pence coins, and 30 pennies.
You can keep them in an envelope or a clear zip-top wallet.

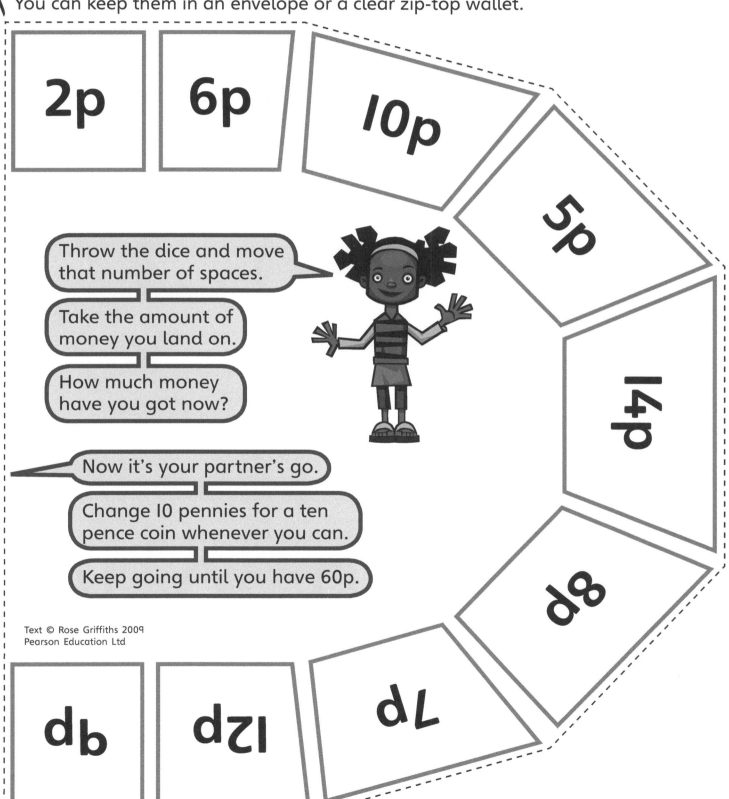

Throw the dice and move that number of spaces.

Take the amount of money you land on.

How much money have you got now?

Now it's your partner's go.

Change 10 pennies for a ten pence coin whenever you can.

Keep going until you have 60p.

2p 6p 10p 5p 14p 8p 7p 12p 9p

Text © Rose Griffiths 2009
Pearson Education Ltd

G T ◀ Blue Pupil Book Part 2; use from pages
38 and 39 onwards
Text © Rose Griffiths 2009
Pearson Education Ltd
B57

Tens and ones game

Print these on card. You can use them again.
Cut out the instructions card, playing board and 10 number cards.
You can keep them in an envelope or a clear zip-top wallet.

Tens and ones

A game for 1, 2 or 3 people.

- **Before you start**
  You need a counter each. Put your counter on 0.
  Shuffle the number cards. Put them in a pile, face down.

- **How to play**

Take a card.
Move your counter that number of spaces.

Put the card on the bottom of the pile.

Now it is your partner's go.

- **The first counter to get to 60 is the winner.**

Blue Pupil Book Part 2: **Counting in 10s and 1s to 60**

Text © Rose Griffiths 2009
Pearson Education Ltd

Tens and ones	Tens and ones	Tens and ones	Tens and ones	Tens and ones
10	10	10	10	10
Tens and ones	Tens and ones	Tens and ones	Tens and ones	Tens and ones
1	1	1	1	1

Text © Rose Griffiths 2009
Pearson Education Ltd
◀ Blue Pupil Book Part 2: use from pages
42 and 43 onwards
T G

Tens and ones game

Print these on card. You can use them again.

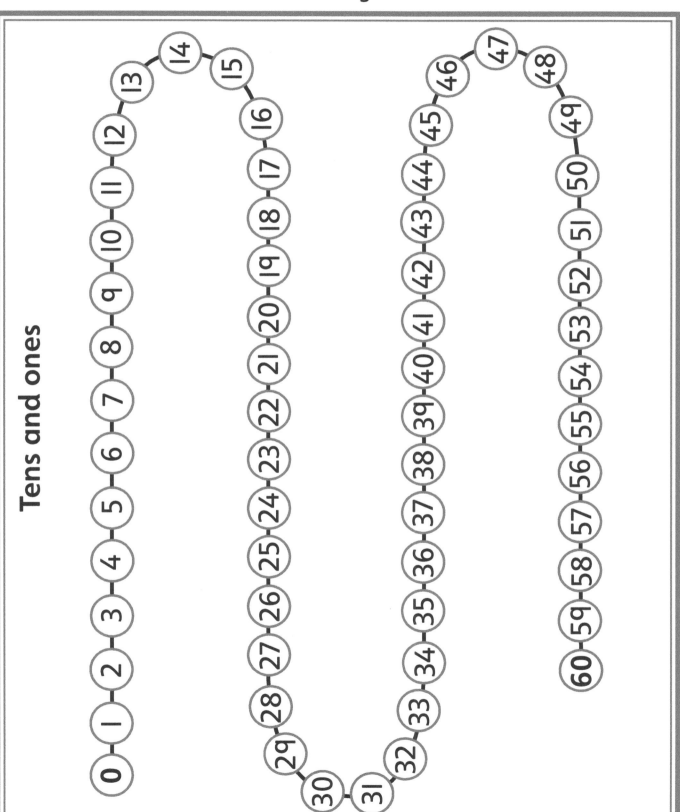

Tens and ones

Text © Rose Griffiths 2009
Pearson Education Ltd

G T

B59

Make 9 game

Print these on card. You can use them again.
Cut out the instructions card and 20 playing cards.
You can keep them in an envelope or a clear zip-top wallet.

Make 9

A game for 1, 2 or 3 people.

- **Before you start**
  Shuffle the cards.
  Spread them out on the table, face down.

- **How to play**

Turn over 2 cards.
Add up the numbers.

If you get exactly 9,
<u>keep</u> the cards.
If not, turn the cards
back over.

Now it is your
partner's go.

- **Keep going until all the cards have gone.**

Blue Pupil Book Part 2; **Addition bonds to 9**

Text © Rose Griffiths 2009
Pearson Education Ltd

Make 9	Make 9	Make 9	Make 9
5	4	5	4

Addition bonds to 9

◀ Blue Pupil Book Part 2; use from
pages 48 and 49 onwards

T

sheet 2 of 2
Print these on card. You can use them again.

Make 9 **5**	Make 9 **4**	Make 9 **6**	Make 9 **3**
Make 9 **6**	Make 9 **3**	Make 9 **6**	Make 9 **3**
Make 9 **7**	Make 9 **2**	Make 9 **7**	Make 9 **2**
Make 9 **8**	Make 9 **1**	Make 9 **9**	Make 9 **0**

Name: _____   Date: _____

Joke shop

Draw the missing eyeballs.

50 bouncing eyeballs!

Draw the missing ants.

60 busy ants!

Text © Rose Griffiths 2009
Pearson Education Ltd
Counting to 75   ◀ Blue Pupil Book Part 3 pages 68 and 69

Tens and teens

Fill in the
missing letters.

30

t h i r t y
t h i r ___
t h ____
t _____
_____
t h i r t y

40

f o r t y
f o r ___
f _____
_____
f o r t y

50

f i f t y
f i f ___
f i ___
f _____
_____
f i f t y

60

s i x t y
s i x ___
s i ____
s _____
_____
s i x t y

70

s e v e n t y
s e v e n ___
s e v _____
s _____
_____
s e v e n t y

Mixed up numbers! Sort them out.

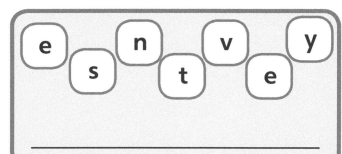

_____

_____

◄ Blue Pupil Book Part 3 pages 70 and 71
Copymaster B64

Spelling thirty to seventy

Text © Rose Griffiths 2009
Pearson Education Ltd

B63

Tens and teens

Draw tens and ones.
Write the number.

thirteen

13

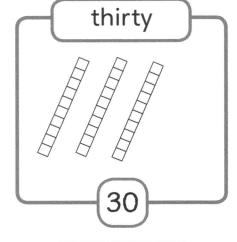

thirty

30

seventy

forty

fifteen

fourteen

seventeen

sixty

Write these numbers as words.

50 _____

16 _____

What comes next?

Join the dots.
They go up in twos.

28
6
0   2   4   8
26 24   10
22   12
                    14
20
16
18

Join the dots.
They go up in fives.

0
15
5   10
40
20
35   25
30

Join the dots.
They go up in tens.

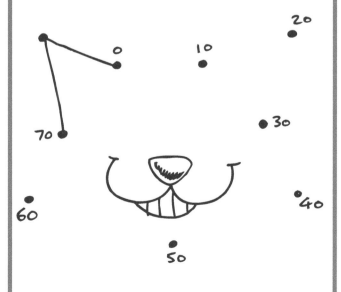

20
0   10
30
70
40
60
50

Draw eyes and whiskers.

Join the dots.
They go <u>down</u> in fives.

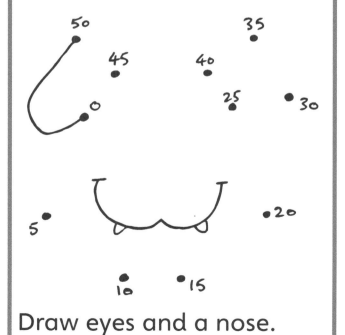

50   35
45   40
0   25   30
5   20
10   15

Draw eyes and a nose.

Name: _____ Date: _____

What comes next?

Fill in the missing numbers.

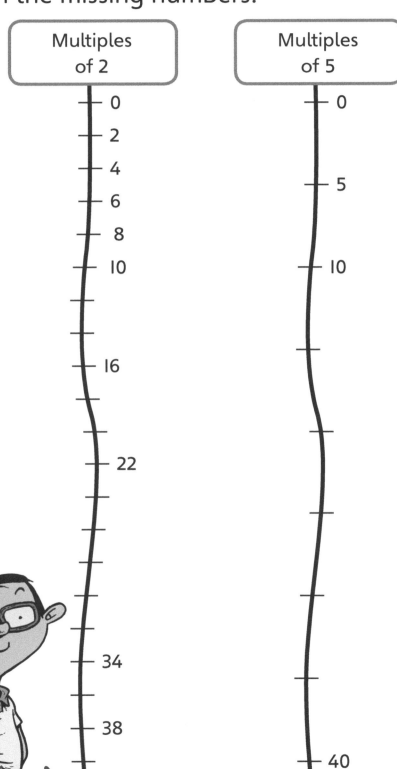

Multiples of 2	Multiples of 5	Multiples of 10
0	0	0
2		
4	5	
6		
8		
10	10	10
16		
22		
34		
38		
	40	

What do you notice about 10, 20, 30 and 40?

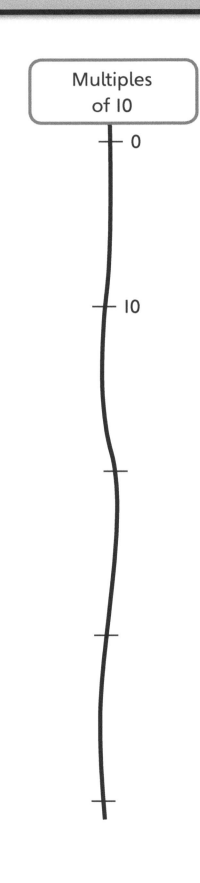

Footballs

Fill in the missing numbers.

3 + ☐ = 10

5 + ☐ = 10

4 + ☐ = 10

2 + ☐ = 10

6 + ☐ = 10

9 + ☐ = 10

7 + ☐ = 10

8 + ☐ = 10

1 + ☐ = 10

☐ + 1 = 10

☐ + 0 = 10

☐ + 4 = 10

☐ + 5 = 10

☐ + 7 = 10

☐ + 2 = 10

☐ + 8 = 10

☐ + 6 = 10

☐ + 3 = 10

6 + ☐ = 10

☐ + 6 = 10

3 + ☐ = 10

☐ + 3 = 10

8 + ☐ = 10

☐ + 8 = 10

1 + ☐ = 10

☐ + 1 = 10

Footballs

Do these as quickly as you can.

10 – 2 = _____	10 – 7 = _____	10 – 1 = _____
10 – 3 = _____	10 – 0 = _____	10 – 8 = _____
10 – 9 = _____	10 – 5 = _____	10 – 4 = _____
10 – 4 = _____	10 – 6 = _____	10 – 3 = _____
10 – 8 = _____	10 – 2 = _____	10 – 7 = _____

 ✔ or ✘

How much change?

How much change?

How much change?

How much change?

Text © Rose Griffiths 2009
Pearson Education Ltd

Addition and subtraction bonds to 10

◀ Blue Pupil Book Part 3 pages 74 and 75

Easier adding

Find tens if you can, to help you.

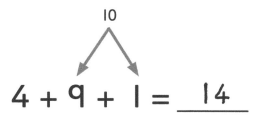

4 + 9 + 1 = __14__

3 + 5 + 7 = ____

2 + 8 + 9 = ____

13 + 4 + 6 = ____

5 + 9 + 5 = ____

6 + 15 + 4 = ____

8 + 11 + 2 = ____

5 + 6 + 7 = ____

9 + 1 + 13 = ____

7 + 9 + 3 = ____

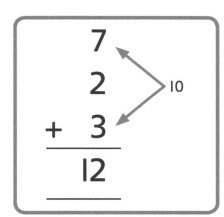

Look for tens.

4	12	6	8
8	3	11	14
+ 6	+ 7	+ 4	+ 2
____	____	____	____
____	____	____	____

 ✔ or ✗

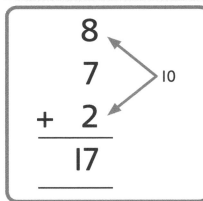

Find tens if you can.

```
    7              2             13             5
    5             15              9             7
  + 5           + 7           + 1           + 3
  ____          ____          ____          ____

  ____          ____          ____          ____


    8              7             14            11
    6             12              3             5
  + 2           + 3           + 6           + 9
  ____          ____          ____          ____

  ____          ____          ____          ____


    5              6              9            13
   15              8              1             5
  + 5           + 4           + 9           + 8
  ____          ____          ____          ____

  ____          ____          ____          ____
```

$4 + 2 + 8 + 6 =$ _____ $3 + 1 + 7 + 9 =$ _____

Name: _____ Date: _____

Speedy sums G   1 2 3 minute test

5 + 4 = _____   9 – 5 = _____   4 + 4 = _____

2 + 8 = _____   7 – 6 = _____   5 – 2 = _____

3 + 3 = _____   4 – 4 = _____   6 + 3 = _____

8 + 0 = _____   10 – 8 = _____   9 – 7 = _____

1 + 6 = _____   7 – 3 = _____   5 + 5 = _____

6 + 4 = _____   8 – 3 = _____   8 – 5 = _____

3 + 7 = _____   2 – 1 = _____   Score: _____

Name: _____ Date: _____

Speedy sums H   1 2 3 minute test

9 + 1 = _____   6 – 1 = _____   4 + 6 = _____

2 + 6 = _____   8 – 5 = _____   9 – 2 = _____

5 + 2 = _____   7 – 2 = _____   0 + 10 = _____

3 + 3 = _____   10 – 2 = _____   7 – 3 = _____

7 + 3 = _____   9 – 8 = _____   3 + 6 = _____

4 + 3 = _____   5 – 5 = _____   10 – 5 = _____

5 + 4 = _____   8 – 4 = _____   Score: _____

Name: _____ Date: _____

Adding up

Use tens and ones.

15 + 19

15 + 19 =

23 + 16

23 + 16 =

16 + 12

16 + 12 =

13 + 27

13 + 27 =

Draw tens and ones.

13 + 20

13 + 20 =

17 + 9

17 + 9 =

14 + 14

14 + 14 =

18 + 5

18 + 5 =

Addition within 40

◄ Blue Pupil Book Part 3 pages 80 and 81
Copymaster B73

Adding up

Use tens and ones. Draw them.

25 + 13

25 + 13 =

19 + 11

19 + 11 =

16 + 16

16 + 16 =

17 + 14

17 + 14 =

Now try these. You can choose how to do them.

15 + 23

21 + 16

7 + 25

20 + 20

B73

Three times table

Cut out the eleven tables facts.
Fold along the dotted line and glue flat.

Ask how to practise with these.

		5 × 3	15
0 × 3	0	6 × 3	18
1 × 3	3	7 × 3	21
2 × 3	6	8 × 3	24
3 × 3	9	9 × 3	27
4 × 3	12	10 × 3	30

Text © Rose Griffiths 2009
Pearson Education Ltd

Three times table

◀ Blue Pupil Book Part 3 pages 82 and 83
Copymaster B75

T

Name: _____   Date: _____

Three times table

Fill in the missing numbers.
Check with a calculator.

$10 \times 3 =$ ☐

$3 \times 10 =$ ☐

$4 \times 3 =$ ☐

$3 \times 4 =$ ☐

$7 \times 3 =$ ☐

$3 \times 7 =$ ☐

$5 \times 3 =$ ☐

$3 \times 5 =$ ☐

$10 \times 3 =$ ☐

☐ $\times 3 = 27$

$8 \times 3 =$ ☐

$7 \times 3 =$ ☐

☐ $\times 3 = 18$

☐ $\times 3 = 15$

$4 \times 3 =$ ☐

☐ $\times 3 = 9$

$2 \times 3 =$ ☐

$1 \times 3 =$ ☐

$0 \times 3 =$ ☐

What is 6 times 3?

What is 3 times 6?

_____   _____

Fifty pences

Draw the missing coins: <u>or</u>

£1·50

£3·50

£5·00

£1·50

How much money is in each box?

£

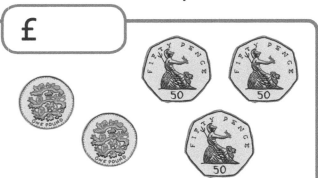

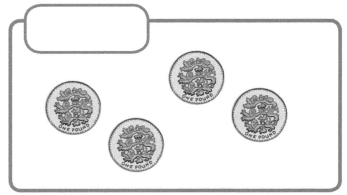

Name: _____   Date: _____

Fifty pences

Use coins.

Draw 4 different ways of making 50p.

50p	50p
50p	50p

Name: _____ Date: _____

Dog's toys

Dog toys £2 each

How many toys for £4?

Put the pounds in twos.

$4 \div 2 =$ _____

How many toys for £6?

$6 \div 2 =$ _____

How many toys for £8?

$8 \div 2 =$ _____

How many toys for £10?

$10 \div 2 =$ _____

How many toys for £12?

$12 \div 2 =$ _____

B78

Text © Rose Griffiths 2009
Pearson Education Ltd

Multiplication and division by 2

◄ Blue Pupil Book Part 3 pages 86 and 87
Copymaster B79

Dog's toys

Dog toys £2 each

Multiplying

How much for 10 toys?

1 0 × 2 = _____

9 × 2 = _____

8 × 2 = _____

7 × 2 = _____

6 × 2 = _____

5 × 2 = _____

4 × 2 = _____

3 × 2 = _____

2 × 2 = _____

1 × 2 = _____

Dividing

How many toys for £20?

2 0 ÷ 2 = _____

1 8 ÷ 2 = _____

1 6 ÷ 2 = _____

1 4 ÷ 2 = _____

1 2 ÷ 2 = _____

1 0 ÷ 2 = _____

8 ÷ 2 = _____

6 ÷ 2 = _____

4 ÷ 2 = _____

2 ÷ 2 = _____

Swimming

Fill in the missing numbers.

10	20		
9		29	
8		28	
	17		37
6	16		36
5		25	35
	14	24	
3	13		33
2		22	32
1	11	21	

Now do the questions on Pupil Book page 89.

Text © Rose Griffiths 2009
Pearson Education Ltd

Mixed problems

◄ Blue Pupil Book Part 3 pages 88 and 89
Copymaster B81

Swimming

Fill in the missing letters.

1st	2nd	3rd	4th
f i r s t	s e c o n d	t h i r d	f o u r t h
f i r ___	s e c _____	t h ___	f o u r ___
f _____	s _____	t _____	f _____
f _____	s _____	t _____	f _____
_____	_____	_____	_____
f i r s t	s e c o n d	t h i r d	f o u r t h

We had a swimming race.

Finish writing these.

I came first.

1 st
PRIZE

I came second.

PRIZE

I came third.

PRIZE

I came fourth.

PRIZE

Text © Rose Griffiths 2009
Pearson Education Ltd

B81

Dog food

$4 \times 2 =$ _____ $2 \times 4 =$ _____ $7 \times 2 =$ _____

$2 \times 2 =$ _____ $6 \times 2 =$ _____ $9 \times 2 =$ _____

$8 \times 2 =$ _____ $2 \times 7 =$ _____ $2 \times 3 =$ _____

$2 \times 5 =$ _____ $10 \times 2 =$ _____ $5 \times 2 =$ _____

$3 \times 2 =$ _____ $2 \times 9 =$ _____ $2 \times 10 =$ _____

$2 \times 6 =$ _____ $2 \times 8 =$ _____ $1 \times 2 =$ _____

$\boxed{} \times 2 = 6$
$6 \div 2 =$ _____

$\boxed{} \times 2 = 14$
$14 \div 2 =$ _____

$\boxed{} \times 2 = 8$
$8 \div 2 =$ _____

$\boxed{} \times 2 = 18$
$18 \div 2 =$ _____

  ✔ or ✗

Dog food

$\boxed{} \times 2 = 4$

$4 \div 2 = \rule{2cm}{0.4pt}$

$\boxed{} \times 2 = 10$

$10 \div 2 = \rule{2cm}{0.4pt}$

$\boxed{} \times 2 = 12$

$12 \div 2 = \rule{2cm}{0.4pt}$

$\boxed{} \times 2 = 16$

$16 \div 2 = \rule{2cm}{0.4pt}$

$8 \div 2 = \rule{2cm}{0.4pt}$ $6 \div 2 = \rule{2cm}{0.4pt}$ $8 \div 2 = \rule{2cm}{0.4pt}$

$4 \div 2 = \rule{2cm}{0.4pt}$ $16 \div 2 = \rule{2cm}{0.4pt}$ $14 \div 2 = \rule{2cm}{0.4pt}$

$10 \div 2 = \rule{2cm}{0.4pt}$ $4 \div 2 = \rule{2cm}{0.4pt}$ $12 \div 2 = \rule{2cm}{0.4pt}$

$14 \div 2 = \rule{2cm}{0.4pt}$ $20 \div 2 = \rule{2cm}{0.4pt}$ $16 \div 2 = \rule{2cm}{0.4pt}$

$4 \div 2 = \rule{2cm}{0.4pt}$ $18 \div 2 = \rule{2cm}{0.4pt}$ $10 \div 2 = \rule{2cm}{0.4pt}$

$12 \div 2 = \rule{2cm}{0.4pt}$ $2 \div 2 = \rule{2cm}{0.4pt}$ $18 \div 2 = \rule{2cm}{0.4pt}$

 ✔ or ✗

Taking away

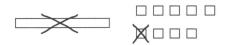

Use tens and ones.

27 – 15

27 – 15 =

19 – 11

19 – 11 =

Cross out tens and ones.

36 – 13

36 – 13 =

28 – 22

28 – 22 =

18 – 7

18 – 7 =

34 – 14

34 – 14 =

27 – 16

27 – 16 =

29 – 14

29 – 14 =

Text © Rose Griffiths 2009
Pearson Education Ltd

Subtraction within 40

◀ Blue Pupil Book Part 3 pages 92 and 93
Copymaster B85

Taking away

Use tens and ones.

How much did each person have left?

I had 39p.
I spent 15p.

He had ☐ left.

I had 40p.
I spent 28p.

She had ☐ left.

I had 31p.
I spent 19p.

She had ☐ left.

I had 26p.
I spent 14p.

He had ☐ left.

I had 30p.
I spent 17p.

He had ☐ left.

I had 35p.
I spent 15p.

She had ☐ left.

I had 40p.
I spent 15p.

He had ☐ left.

I had 23p.
I spent 18p.

He had ☐ left.

Secret numbers

Use cards numbered I to 20.

Which numbers belong in each box?

Even numbers

2	4			

Odd numbers

I	3			

What do you notice about the even numbers and the multiples of 2?

Multiples of 2

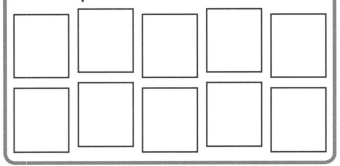

Multiples of 3

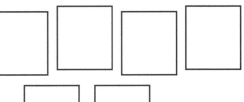

Multiples of 5

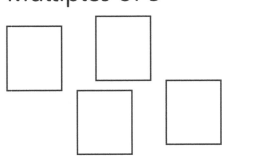

Multiples of 10

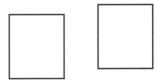

Number properties ◀ Blue Pupil Book Part 3 pages 94 and 95
Copymaster B87

Secret numbers

Use cards numbered 1 to 20.
Make up puzzles. Give them to a friend.

These puzzles are for _____

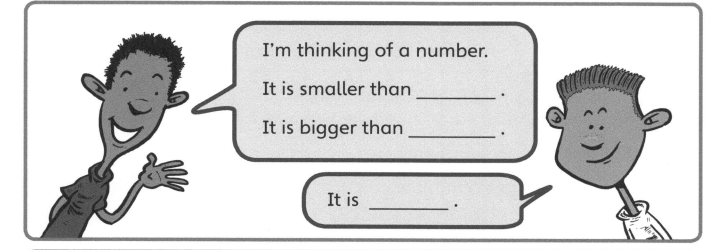

I'm thinking of a number.

It is smaller than _____ .

It is bigger than _____ .

It is _____ .

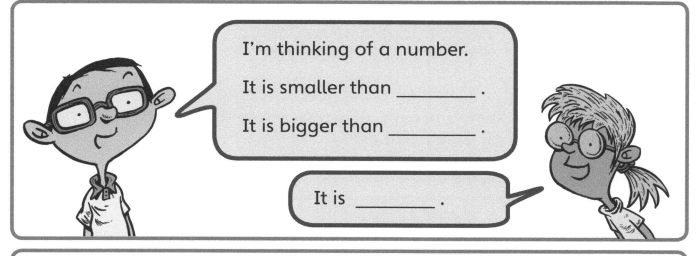

I'm thinking of a number.

It is smaller than _____ .

It is bigger than _____ .

It is _____ .

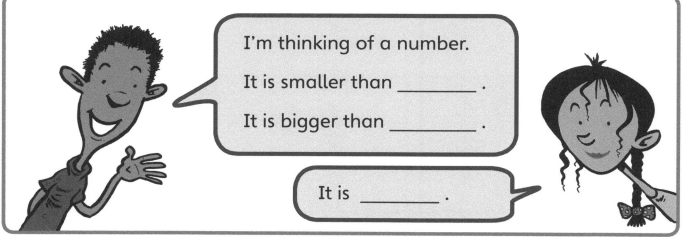

I'm thinking of a number.

It is smaller than _____ .

It is bigger than _____ .

It is _____ .

sheet 1 of 2

Print these on card. You can use them again.

Cut out the instructions card, 10 number cards, and 4 bingo cards. If possible, include 24 counters. You can keep them in an envelope or a clear zip-top wallet.

Tens and teens bingo

> A game for 2, 3 or 4 people.

- **Before you start**
  You need a bingo card and 6 counters each.
  Shuffle the 10 number cards. Put them in a pile, face down.

- **How to play**

Take a number card and read it to everyone.

If that number is on their bingo card, they cover it up with a counter.

Now it is your partner's go.

- **Keep going until someone says 'Bingo' because they have covered up all their numbers.**

Blue Pupil Book Part 3; **Saying and listening to tens and teen numbers**

seventy	Tens and teens bingo	sixty	Tens and teens bingo	fifty	Tens and teens bingo	forty	Tens and teens bingo	thirty	Tens and teens bingo
seventeen	Tens and teens bingo	sixteen	Tens and teens bingo	fifteen	Tens and teens bingo	fourteen	Tens and teens bingo	thirteen	Tens and teens bingo

◀ Blue Pupil Book Part 3; use from pages 70 and 71 onwards (T) (G)

Tens and teens bingo

Print these on card. You can use them again.

Tens and teens bingo

Tens and teens bingo	17 15	60		
	15			
	40	70		
		13		

Tens and teens bingo

		15	
17		40	
14			
30 70	60 50 16		

Tens and teens bingo

50 13		
13		
40 16		
15 70		

Tens and teens bingo

70		
50 16		
17		
30 14		

Text © Rose Griffiths 2009
Pearson Education Ltd

G T

B89

Sums which make 10

Print these on card. You can use them again.
Cut out the instructions cards, 40 number cards, and 3 sum cards.
You can keep them in an envelope or a clear zip-top wallet.

Sums which make 10

> A game for 1, 2 or 3 people.

- **Before you start**
  Take a sum card each.
  Shuffle the number cards.
  Put them in a pile on the table, face down.

- **How to play**
  Can you make 4 different sums which make 10?

> Take the top number card.
> Put it on your sum card,
> or (if you don't want it)
> put it at the bottom of the pile.

> Now it is your partner's go.

- **Keep going until you have all filled your cards.**
  Who finished first?

Blue Pupil Book Part 3; **Addition and subtraction bonds to 10**

Text © Rose Griffiths 2009
Pearson Education Ltd

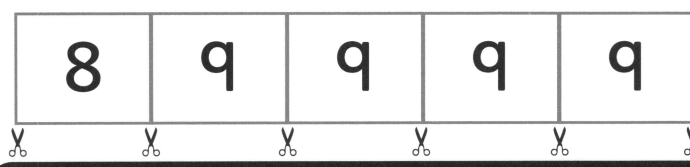

| 8 | 9 | 9 | 9 | 9 |

◀ Blue Pupil Book Part 3; use from pages 74 and 75 onwards

(T) (G)

Sums which make 10

Print these on card. You can use them again.

1	1	2	2	3
1	1	2	2	3
3	4	4	5	5
3	4	4	5	5
5	5	6	6	7
5	5	6	6	7
7	7	8	8	8

B91

Sums which make 10

Print 3 copies on card. You can use them again.

Sums which make 10

☐ + ☐ = 10

☐ + ☐ = 10

☐ + ☐ = 10

☐ + ☐ = 10

◀ Blue Pupil Book Part 3; use from pages 74 and 75 onwards

T G